Created and published by Knock Knock
Distributed by Who's There Inc.
Venice, CA 90291
knockknockstuff.com

ISBN: 978-160106561-2
UPC: 825703-50019-6

20 19 18 17 16 15 14 13 12 11 10 9 8 7 6 5 4 3 2

CUBICLE

Guest Book

KNOCK
KNOCK®
VENICE, CALIFORNIA

Memorable Moments: _____
_____
_____
_____
_____
_____

Additional Sentiments: _____
_____
_____
_____
_____
_____

Welcome to My Cubicle

DATE OF VISIT: ....

TIME OF VISIT: .... AM/PM

TV SHOW THAT BEST DESCRIBES THIS OFFICE:
- ☐ *Lost*
- ☐ *Survivor*
- ☐ *Mad Men*
- ☐ *Freaks and Geeks*
- ☐ *The A-Team*
- ☐ *Modern Family*
- ☐ ....

CUBICLE ACTIVITY BAR GRAPH
Shade in the amount of time spent doing the following:

	NO TIME	LONG TIME
Liaising		
Strategizing		
Brainstorming		
Procrastinating		
Gossiping		

SIGN IN, PLEASE

REASON FOR VISIT: ☐ Business   ☐ Pleasure   ☐ Boredom

HIDDEN AGENDA: ....

CUBICLE DWELLER WAS:
- ☐ At desk
- ☐ Out to lunch
- ☐ In bathroom
- ☐ On coffee break
- ☐ In meeting
- ☐ Asleep
- ☐ Cubicle hopping
- ☐ Who knows
- ☐ ....

CUBICLE ART

☐ Inside the box   ☐ Outside the box

ITEMS TAKEN DURING THIS VISIT:
- ☐ Stapler
- ☐ Scissors
- ☐ Pens
- ☐ Toiletries
- ☐ Gum
- ☐ Candy
- ☐ Food
- ☐ Medication
- ☐ Valuables
- ☐ ....

ITEMS WERE:
- ☐ Given   ☐ "Borrowed"

TAKEAWAY FROM VISIT:
....
....

REPORT CARD	A	B	C	D	F
Ambience					
Cleanliness					
Décor					
Amenities					
Snacks					
Privacy					
Scuttlebutt					
OVERALL					

Memorable Moments: _____

_____

_____

_____

_____

_____

Additional Sentiments: _____

_____

_____

_____

_____

_____

Welcome to My Cubicle

DATE OF VISIT: ....

TIME OF VISIT: .... AM/PM

TV SHOW THAT BEST DESCRIBES THIS OFFICE:
- ☐ *Lost*
- ☐ *Survivor*
- ☐ *Mad Men*
- ☐ *Freaks and Geeks*
- ☐ *The A-Team*
- ☐ *Modern Family*
- ☐ ....

CUBICLE ACTIVITY BAR GRAPH
Shade in the amount of time spent doing the following:

NO TIME   LONG TIME

Liaising

Strategizing

Brainstorming

Procrastinating

Gossiping

SIGN IN, PLEASE

REASON FOR VISIT: ☐ Business   ☐ Pleasure   ☐ Boredom

HIDDEN AGENDA: ....

CUBICLE DWELLER WAS:
- ☐ At desk
- ☐ Out to lunch
- ☐ In bathroom
- ☐ On coffee break
- ☐ In meeting
- ☐ Asleep
- ☐ Cubicle hopping
- ☐ Who knows
- ☐ ....

CUBICLE ART

☐ Inside the box   ☐ Outside the box

ITEMS TAKEN DURING THIS VISIT:
- ☐ Stapler
- ☐ Scissors
- ☐ Pens
- ☐ Toiletries
- ☐ Gum
- ☐ Candy
- ☐ Food
- ☐ Medication
- ☐ Valuables
- ☐ ....

ITEMS WERE:
- ☐ Given
- ☐ "Borrowed"

TAKEAWAY FROM VISIT:
....
....

REPORT CARD	A	B	C	D	F
Ambience					
Cleanliness					
Décor					
Amenities					
Snacks					
Privacy					
Scuttlebutt					
OVERALL					

Memorable Moments: _____

_____

_____

_____

_____

Additional Sentiments: _____

_____

_____

_____

_____

Welcome to My Cubicle

DATE OF VISIT: ....

TIME OF VISIT: .... AM/PM

TV SHOW THAT BEST DESCRIBES THIS OFFICE:

- ☐ *Lost*
- ☐ *Survivor*
- ☐ *Mad Men*
- ☐ *Freaks and Geeks*
- ☐ *The A-Team*
- ☐ *Modern Family*
- ☐ ....

CUBICLE ACTIVITY BAR GRAPH

Shade in the amount of time spent doing the following:

	NO TIME	LONG TIME

Liaising

Strategizing

Brainstorming

Procrastinating

Gossiping

SIGN IN, PLEASE

REASON FOR VISIT: ☐ Business ☐ Pleasure ☐ Boredom

HIDDEN AGENDA: ....

CUBICLE DWELLER WAS:	☐ At desk	☐ On coffee break	☐ Cubicle hopping
	☐ Out to lunch	☐ In meeting	☐ Who knows
	☐ In bathroom	☐ Asleep	☐ ....

CUBICLE ART

☐ Inside the box   ☐ Outside the box

ITEMS TAKEN DURING THIS VISIT:

- ☐ Stapler
- ☐ Scissors
- ☐ Pens
- ☐ Toiletries
- ☐ Gum
- ☐ Candy
- ☐ Food
- ☐ Medication
- ☐ Valuables
- ☐ ....

ITEMS WERE:

☐ Given   ☐ "Borrowed"

TAKEAWAY FROM VISIT:
....
....

REPORT CARD	A	B	C	D	F
Ambience					
Cleanliness					
Décor					
Amenities					
Snacks					
Privacy					
Scuttlebutt					
OVERALL					

Memorable Moments: _____

_____

_____

_____

_____

_____

Additional Sentiments: _____

_____

_____

_____

_____

_____

Welcome to My Cubicle

DATE OF VISIT: ....

TIME OF VISIT: .... AM/PM

TV SHOW THAT BEST DESCRIBES THIS OFFICE:
- ☐ Lost
- ☐ Survivor
- ☐ Mad Men
- ☐ Freaks and Geeks
- ☐ The A-Team
- ☐ Modern Family
- ☐ ....

CUBICLE ACTIVITY BAR GRAPH
Shade in the amount of time spent doing the following:

NO TIME   LONG TIME

Liaising

Strategizing

Brainstorming

Procrastinating

Gossiping

SIGN IN, PLEASE

REASON FOR VISIT: ☐ Business   ☐ Pleasure   ☐ Boredom

HIDDEN AGENDA: ....

CUBICLE DWELLER WAS:
- ☐ At desk
- ☐ Out to lunch
- ☐ In bathroom
- ☐ On coffee break
- ☐ In meeting
- ☐ Asleep
- ☐ Cubicle hopping
- ☐ Who knows
- ☐ ....

CUBICLE ART

☐ Inside the box   ☐ Outside the box

ITEMS TAKEN DURING THIS VISIT:
- ☐ Stapler
- ☐ Scissors
- ☐ Pens
- ☐ Toiletries
- ☐ Gum
- ☐ Candy
- ☐ Food
- ☐ Medication
- ☐ Valuables
- ☐ ....

ITEMS WERE:
- ☐ Given
- ☐ "Borrowed"

TAKEAWAY FROM VISIT:
....
....

REPORT CARD	A	B	C	D	F
Ambience					
Cleanliness					
Décor					
Amenities					
Snacks					
Privacy					
Scuttlebutt					
OVERALL					

Memorable Moments: _____

_____

_____

_____

_____

Additional Sentiments: _____

_____

_____

_____

_____

Welcome to My Cubicle

DATE OF VISIT: ....

TIME OF VISIT: .... AM/PM

TV SHOW THAT BEST DESCRIBES THIS OFFICE:

- ☐ *Lost*
- ☐ *Survivor*
- ☐ *Mad Men*
- ☐ *Freaks and Geeks*
- ☐ *The A-Team*
- ☐ *Modern Family*
- ☐ ....

CUBICLE ACTIVITY BAR GRAPH

Shade in the amount of time spent doing the following:

	NO TIME	LONG TIME
Liaising		
Strategizing		
Brainstorming		
Procrastinating		
Gossiping		

SIGN IN, PLEASE

REASON FOR VISIT: ☐ Business   ☐ Pleasure   ☐ Boredom

HIDDEN AGENDA: ....

CUBICLE DWELLER WAS:	☐ At desk	☐ On coffee break	☐ Cubicle hopping
	☐ Out to lunch	☐ In meeting	☐ Who knows
	☐ In bathroom	☐ Asleep	☐ ....

CUBICLE ART

☐ Inside the box   ☐ Outside the box

ITEMS TAKEN DURING THIS VISIT:

- ☐ Stapler
- ☐ Scissors
- ☐ Pens
- ☐ Toiletries
- ☐ Gum
- ☐ Candy
- ☐ Food
- ☐ Medication
- ☐ Valuables
- ☐ ....

ITEMS WERE:

☐ Given   ☐ "Borrowed"

TAKEAWAY FROM VISIT:

....
....

REPORT CARD	A	B	C	D	F
Ambience					
Cleanliness					
Décor					
Amenities					
Snacks					
Privacy					
Scuttlebutt					
OVERALL					

Memorable Moments: _____

_____

_____

_____

_____

Additional Sentiments: _____

_____

_____

_____

_____

Welcome to My Cubicle

DATE OF VISIT: ....

TIME OF VISIT: .... AM/PM

TV SHOW THAT BEST DESCRIBES THIS OFFICE:

- ☐ *Lost*
- ☐ *Survivor*
- ☐ *Mad Men*
- ☐ *Freaks and Geeks*
- ☐ *The A-Team*
- ☐ *Modern Family*
- ☐ ....

CUBICLE ACTIVITY BAR GRAPH

Shade in the amount of time spent doing the following:

	NO TIME	LONG TIME

Liaising

Strategizing

Brainstorming

Procrastinating

Gossiping

SIGN IN, PLEASE

REASON FOR VISIT: ☐ Business   ☐ Pleasure   ☐ Boredom

HIDDEN AGENDA: ....

CUBICLE DWELLER WAS:	☐ At desk	☐ On coffee break	☐ Cubicle hopping
	☐ Out to lunch	☐ In meeting	☐ Who knows
	☐ In bathroom	☐ Asleep	☐ ....

CUBICLE ART

☐ Inside the box   ☐ Outside the box

ITEMS TAKEN DURING THIS VISIT:

- ☐ Stapler
- ☐ Scissors
- ☐ Pens
- ☐ Toiletries
- ☐ Gum
- ☐ Candy
- ☐ Food
- ☐ Medication
- ☐ Valuables
- ☐ ....

ITEMS WERE:

☐ Given   ☐ "Borrowed"

TAKEAWAY FROM VISIT:

....
....

REPORT CARD	A	B	C	D	F
Ambience					
Cleanliness					
Décor					
Amenities					
Snacks					
Privacy					
Scuttlebutt					
OVERALL					

Memorable Moments: _____

_____

_____

_____

_____

_____

Additional Sentiments: _____

_____

_____

_____

_____

_____

Welcome to My Cubicle

DATE OF VISIT: ....

TIME OF VISIT: .... AM/PM

TV SHOW THAT BEST DESCRIBES THIS OFFICE:

☐ *Lost*
☐ *Survivor*
☐ *Mad Men*
☐ *Freaks and Geeks*
☐ *The A-Team*
☐ *Modern Family*
☐ ....

CUBICLE ACTIVITY BAR GRAPH

Shade in the amount of time spent doing the following:

	NO TIME	LONG TIME

Liaising

Strategizing

Brainstorming

Procrastinating

Gossiping

SIGN IN, PLEASE

REASON FOR VISIT: ☐ Business   ☐ Pleasure   ☐ Boredom

HIDDEN AGENDA: ....

CUBICLE DWELLER WAS:
☐ At desk   ☐ On coffee break   ☐ Cubicle hopping
☐ Out to lunch   ☐ In meeting   ☐ Who knows
☐ In bathroom   ☐ Asleep   ☐ ....

CUBICLE ART

☐ Inside the box   ☐ Outside the box

ITEMS TAKEN DURING THIS VISIT:

☐ Stapler   ☐ Candy
☐ Scissors   ☐ Food
☐ Pens   ☐ Medication
☐ Toiletries   ☐ Valuables
☐ Gum   ☐ ....

ITEMS WERE:

☐ Given   ☐ "Borrowed"

TAKEAWAY FROM VISIT:

....
....

REPORT CARD	A	B	C	D	F
Ambience					
Cleanliness					
Décor					
Amenities					
Snacks					
Privacy					
Scuttlebutt					
OVERALL					

Memorable Moments: _____

_____

_____

_____

_____

Additional Sentiments: _____

_____

_____

_____

_____

Welcome to My Cubicle

DATE OF VISIT: ....

TIME OF VISIT: .... AM/PM

TV SHOW THAT BEST DESCRIBES THIS OFFICE:
- ☐ *Lost*
- ☐ *Survivor*
- ☐ *Mad Men*
- ☐ *Freaks and Geeks*
- ☐ *The A-Team*
- ☐ *Modern Family*
- ☐ ....

CUBICLE ACTIVITY BAR GRAPH
Shade in the amount of time spent doing the following:

	NO TIME	LONG TIME
Liaising		
Strategizing		
Brainstorming		
Procrastinating		
Gossiping		

SIGN IN, PLEASE

REASON FOR VISIT: ☐ Business   ☐ Pleasure   ☐ Boredom

HIDDEN AGENDA: ....

CUBICLE DWELLER WAS:	☐ At desk	☐ On coffee break	☐ Cubicle hopping
	☐ Out to lunch	☐ In meeting	☐ Who knows
	☐ In bathroom	☐ Asleep	☐ ....

CUBICLE ART

☐ Inside the box   ☐ Outside the box

ITEMS TAKEN DURING THIS VISIT:
- ☐ Stapler
- ☐ Scissors
- ☐ Pens
- ☐ Toiletries
- ☐ Gum
- ☐ Candy
- ☐ Food
- ☐ Medication
- ☐ Valuables
- ☐ ....

ITEMS WERE:

☐ Given   ☐ "Borrowed"

TAKEAWAY FROM VISIT:
....
....

REPORT CARD	A	B	C	D	F
Ambience					
Cleanliness					
Décor					
Amenities					
Snacks					
Privacy					
Scuttlebutt					
OVERALL					

Memorable Moments: _____

_____

_____

_____

_____

_____

Additional Sentiments: _____

_____

_____

_____

_____

_____

Welcome to My Cubicle

DATE OF VISIT: ....

TIME OF VISIT: .... AM/PM

TV SHOW THAT BEST DESCRIBES THIS OFFICE:

☐ *Lost*
☐ *Survivor*
☐ *Mad Men*
☐ *Freaks and Geeks*
☐ *The A-Team*
☐ *Modern Family*
☐ ....

CUBICLE ACTIVITY BAR GRAPH

Shade in the amount of time spent doing the following:

	NO TIME	LONG TIME
Liaising		
Strategizing		
Brainstorming		
Procrastinating		
Gossiping		

SIGN IN, PLEASE

REASON FOR VISIT: ☐ Business   ☐ Pleasure   ☐ Boredom

HIDDEN AGENDA: ....

CUBICLE DWELLER WAS:	☐ At desk	☐ On coffee break	☐ Cubicle hopping
	☐ Out to lunch	☐ In meeting	☐ Who knows
	☐ In bathroom	☐ Asleep	☐ ....

CUBICLE ART

☐ Inside the box   ☐ Outside the box

ITEMS TAKEN DURING THIS VISIT:

☐ Stapler   ☐ Candy
☐ Scissors   ☐ Food
☐ Pens   ☐ Medication
☐ Toiletries   ☐ Valuables
☐ Gum   ☐ ....

ITEMS WERE:

☐ Given   ☐ "Borrowed"

TAKEAWAY FROM VISIT:

....
....

REPORT CARD	A	B	C	D	F
Ambience					
Cleanliness					
Décor					
Amenities					
Snacks					
Privacy					
Scuttlebutt					
OVERALL					

Memorable Moments: _____

_____

_____

_____

_____

_____

Additional Sentiments: _____

_____

_____

_____

_____

_____

Welcome to My Cubicle

DATE OF VISIT: ....

TIME OF VISIT: .... AM/PM

TV SHOW THAT BEST DESCRIBES THIS OFFICE:
- ☐ *Lost*
- ☐ *Survivor*
- ☐ *Mad Men*
- ☐ *Freaks and Geeks*
- ☐ *The A-Team*
- ☐ *Modern Family*
- ☐ ....

CUBICLE ACTIVITY BAR GRAPH
Shade in the amount of time spent doing the following:

	NO TIME	LONG TIME
Liaising		
Strategizing		
Brainstorming		
Procrastinating		
Gossiping		

SIGN IN, PLEASE

REASON FOR VISIT: ☐ Business   ☐ Pleasure   ☐ Boredom

HIDDEN AGENDA: ....

CUBICLE DWELLER WAS:	☐ At desk	☐ On coffee break	☐ Cubicle hopping
	☐ Out to lunch	☐ In meeting	☐ Who knows
	☐ In bathroom	☐ Asleep	☐ ....

CUBICLE ART

☐ Inside the box   ☐ Outside the box

ITEMS TAKEN DURING THIS VISIT:
- ☐ Stapler   ☐ Candy
- ☐ Scissors   ☐ Food
- ☐ Pens   ☐ Medication
- ☐ Toiletries   ☐ Valuables
- ☐ Gum   ☐ ....

ITEMS WERE:
☐ Given   ☐ "Borrowed"

TAKEAWAY FROM VISIT:
....
....

REPORT CARD	A	B	C	D	F
Ambience					
Cleanliness					
Décor					
Amenities					
Snacks					
Privacy					
Scuttlebutt					
OVERALL					

Memorable Moments: _____

_____

_____

_____

_____

Additional Sentiments: _____

_____

_____

_____

_____

Welcome to My Cubicle

DATE OF VISIT: ....

TIME OF VISIT: .... AM/PM

TV SHOW THAT BEST DESCRIBES THIS OFFICE:

- ☐ *Lost*
- ☐ *Survivor*
- ☐ *Mad Men*
- ☐ *Freaks and Geeks*
- ☐ *The A-Team*
- ☐ *Modern Family*
- ☐ ....

CUBICLE ACTIVITY BAR GRAPH

Shade in the amount of time spent doing the following:

	NO TIME	LONG TIME
Liaising		
Strategizing		
Brainstorming		
Procrastinating		
Gossiping		

SIGN IN, PLEASE

REASON FOR VISIT: ☐ Business   ☐ Pleasure   ☐ Boredom

HIDDEN AGENDA: ....

CUBICLE DWELLER WAS:	☐ At desk	☐ On coffee break	☐ Cubicle hopping
	☐ Out to lunch	☐ In meeting	☐ Who knows
	☐ In bathroom	☐ Asleep	☐ ....

CUBICLE ART

☐ Inside the box   ☐ Outside the box

ITEMS TAKEN DURING THIS VISIT:

- ☐ Stapler
- ☐ Scissors
- ☐ Pens
- ☐ Toiletries
- ☐ Gum
- ☐ Candy
- ☐ Food
- ☐ Medication
- ☐ Valuables
- ☐ ....

ITEMS WERE:

☐ Given   ☐ "Borrowed"

TAKEAWAY FROM VISIT:
....
....

REPORT CARD	A	B	C	D	F
Ambience					
Cleanliness					
Décor					
Amenities					
Snacks					
Privacy					
Scuttlebutt					
OVERALL					

Memorable Moments: _____

_____

_____

_____

_____

_____

Additional Sentiments: _____

_____

_____

_____

_____

_____

Welcome to My Cubicle

DATE OF VISIT: ....

TIME OF VISIT: .... AM/PM

TV SHOW THAT BEST DESCRIBES THIS OFFICE:
- ☐ *Lost*
- ☐ *Survivor*
- ☐ *Mad Men*
- ☐ *Freaks and Geeks*
- ☐ *The A-Team*
- ☐ *Modern Family*
- ☐ ....

CUBICLE ACTIVITY BAR GRAPH
Shade in the amount of time spent doing the following:

	NO TIME	LONG TIME
Liaising		
Strategizing		
Brainstorming		
Procrastinating		
Gossiping		

SIGN IN, PLEASE

REASON FOR VISIT: ☐ Business ☐ Pleasure ☐ Boredom

HIDDEN AGENDA: ....

CUBICLE DWELLER WAS:	☐ At desk	☐ On coffee break	☐ Cubicle hopping
	☐ Out to lunch	☐ In meeting	☐ Who knows
	☐ In bathroom	☐ Asleep	☐ ....

CUBICLE ART

☐ Inside the box   ☐ Outside the box

ITEMS TAKEN DURING THIS VISIT:
- ☐ Stapler
- ☐ Scissors
- ☐ Pens
- ☐ Toiletries
- ☐ Gum
- ☐ Candy
- ☐ Food
- ☐ Medication
- ☐ Valuables
- ☐ ....

ITEMS WERE:
☐ Given   ☐ "Borrowed"

TAKEAWAY FROM VISIT:
....
....

REPORT CARD	A	B	C	D	F
Ambience					
Cleanliness					
Décor					
Amenities					
Snacks					
Privacy					
Scuttlebutt					
OVERALL					

Memorable Moments: _____

_____
_____
_____
_____

Additional Sentiments: _____

_____
_____
_____
_____

Welcome to My Cubicle

DATE OF VISIT: ....

TIME OF VISIT: .... AM/PM

TV SHOW THAT BEST DESCRIBES THIS OFFICE:
- ☐ *Lost*
- ☐ *Survivor*
- ☐ *Mad Men*
- ☐ *Freaks and Geeks*
- ☐ *The A-Team*
- ☐ *Modern Family*
- ☐ ....

CUBICLE ACTIVITY BAR GRAPH
Shade in the amount of time spent doing the following:

NO TIME   LONG TIME

Liaising

Strategizing

Brainstorming

Procrastinating

Gossiping

SIGN IN, PLEASE

REASON FOR VISIT: ☐ Business   ☐ Pleasure   ☐ Boredom

HIDDEN AGENDA: ....

CUBICLE DWELLER WAS:
- ☐ At desk
- ☐ Out to lunch
- ☐ In bathroom
- ☐ On coffee break
- ☐ In meeting
- ☐ Asleep
- ☐ Cubicle hopping
- ☐ Who knows
- ☐ ....

CUBICLE ART

☐ Inside the box   ☐ Outside the box

ITEMS TAKEN DURING THIS VISIT:
- ☐ Stapler
- ☐ Scissors
- ☐ Pens
- ☐ Toiletries
- ☐ Gum
- ☐ Candy
- ☐ Food
- ☐ Medication
- ☐ Valuables
- ☐ ....

ITEMS WERE:
☐ Given   ☐ "Borrowed"

TAKEAWAY FROM VISIT:
....
....

REPORT CARD	A	B	C	D	F
Ambience					
Cleanliness					
Décor					
Amenities					
Snacks					
Privacy					
Scuttlebutt					
OVERALL					

Memorable Moments: _____

_____

_____

_____

_____

_____

Additional Sentiments: _____

_____

_____

_____

_____

_____

Welcome to My Cubicle

DATE OF VISIT: ....

TIME OF VISIT: .... AM/PM

TV SHOW THAT BEST DESCRIBES THIS OFFICE:

- ☐ *Lost*
- ☐ *Survivor*
- ☐ *Mad Men*
- ☐ *Freaks and Geeks*
- ☐ *The A-Team*
- ☐ *Modern Family*
- ☐ ....

CUBICLE ACTIVITY BAR GRAPH

Shade in the amount of time spent doing the following:

	NO TIME	LONG TIME

Liaising

Strategizing

Brainstorming

Procrastinating

Gossiping

SIGN IN, PLEASE

REASON FOR VISIT: ☐ Business   ☐ Pleasure   ☐ Boredom

HIDDEN AGENDA: ....

CUBICLE DWELLER WAS:	☐ At desk	☐ On coffee break	☐ Cubicle hopping
	☐ Out to lunch	☐ In meeting	☐ Who knows
	☐ In bathroom	☐ Asleep	☐ ....

CUBICLE ART

☐ Inside the box   ☐ Outside the box

ITEMS TAKEN DURING THIS VISIT:

- ☐ Stapler
- ☐ Scissors
- ☐ Pens
- ☐ Toiletries
- ☐ Gum
- ☐ Candy
- ☐ Food
- ☐ Medication
- ☐ Valuables
- ☐ ....

ITEMS WERE:

☐ Given   ☐ "Borrowed"

TAKEAWAY FROM VISIT:

....
....

REPORT CARD	A	B	C	D	F
Ambience					
Cleanliness					
Décor					
Amenities					
Snacks					
Privacy					
Scuttlebutt					
OVERALL					

Memorable Moments: _____

_____

_____

_____

_____

_____

Additional Sentiments: _____

_____

_____

_____

_____

_____

Welcome to My Cubicle

DATE OF VISIT: ....

TIME OF VISIT: .... AM/PM

TV SHOW THAT BEST DESCRIBES THIS OFFICE:
- ☐ *Lost*
- ☐ *Survivor*
- ☐ *Mad Men*
- ☐ *Freaks and Geeks*
- ☐ *The A-Team*
- ☐ *Modern Family*
- ☐ ....

CUBICLE ACTIVITY BAR GRAPH
Shade in the amount of time spent doing the following:

	NO TIME	LONG TIME
Liaising		
Strategizing		
Brainstorming		
Procrastinating		
Gossiping		

SIGN IN, PLEASE

REASON FOR VISIT: ☐ Business   ☐ Pleasure   ☐ Boredom

HIDDEN AGENDA: ....

CUBICLE DWELLER WAS:	☐ At desk	☐ On coffee break	☐ Cubicle hopping
	☐ Out to lunch	☐ In meeting	☐ Who knows
	☐ In bathroom	☐ Asleep	☐ ....

CUBICLE ART

☐ Inside the box   ☐ Outside the box

ITEMS TAKEN DURING THIS VISIT:
- ☐ Stapler   ☐ Candy
- ☐ Scissors   ☐ Food
- ☐ Pens   ☐ Medication
- ☐ Toiletries   ☐ Valuables
- ☐ Gum   ☐ ....

ITEMS WERE:
- ☐ Given   ☐ "Borrowed"

TAKEAWAY FROM VISIT:
....
....

REPORT CARD	A	B	C	D	F
Ambience					
Cleanliness					
Décor					
Amenities					
Snacks					
Privacy					
Scuttlebutt					
OVERALL					

Memorable Moments: _____

_____

_____

_____

_____

_____

Additional Sentiments: _____

_____

_____

_____

_____

_____

Welcome to My Cubicle

DATE OF VISIT: ....

TIME OF VISIT: .... AM/PM

TV SHOW THAT BEST DESCRIBES THIS OFFICE:
- ☐ *Lost*
- ☐ *Survivor*
- ☐ *Mad Men*
- ☐ *Freaks and Geeks*
- ☐ *The A-Team*
- ☐ *Modern Family*
- ☐ ....

CUBICLE ACTIVITY BAR GRAPH
Shade in the amount of time spent doing the following:

NO TIME   LONG TIME

Liaising

Strategizing

Brainstorming

Procrastinating

Gossiping

SIGN IN, PLEASE

REASON FOR VISIT: ☐ Business   ☐ Pleasure   ☐ Boredom

HIDDEN AGENDA: ....

CUBICLE DWELLER WAS:	☐ At desk	☐ On coffee break	☐ Cubicle hopping
	☐ Out to lunch	☐ In meeting	☐ Who knows
	☐ In bathroom	☐ Asleep	☐ ....

CUBICLE ART

☐ Inside the box   ☐ Outside the box

ITEMS TAKEN DURING THIS VISIT:
- ☐ Stapler
- ☐ Scissors
- ☐ Pens
- ☐ Toiletries
- ☐ Gum
- ☐ Candy
- ☐ Food
- ☐ Medication
- ☐ Valuables
- ☐ ....

ITEMS WERE:
☐ Given   ☐ "Borrowed"

TAKEAWAY FROM VISIT:
....
....

REPORT CARD	A	B	C	D	F
Ambience					
Cleanliness					
Décor					
Amenities					
Snacks					
Privacy					
Scuttlebutt					
OVERALL					

Memorable Moments: _____

_____

_____

_____

_____

_____

Additional Sentiments: _____

_____

_____

_____

_____

_____

Welcome to My Cubicle

DATE OF VISIT: ....

TIME OF VISIT: .... AM/PM

TV SHOW THAT BEST DESCRIBES THIS OFFICE:
- ☐ *Lost*
- ☐ *Survivor*
- ☐ *Mad Men*
- ☐ *Freaks and Geeks*
- ☐ *The A-Team*
- ☐ *Modern Family*
- ☐ ....

CUBICLE ACTIVITY BAR GRAPH
Shade in the amount of time spent doing the following:

NO TIME   LONG TIME

Liaising

Strategizing

Brainstorming

Procrastinating

Gossiping

SIGN IN, PLEASE

REASON FOR VISIT: ☐ Business   ☐ Pleasure   ☐ Boredom

HIDDEN AGENDA: ....

CUBICLE DWELLER WAS:	☐ At desk	☐ On coffee break	☐ Cubicle hopping
	☐ Out to lunch	☐ In meeting	☐ Who knows
	☐ In bathroom	☐ Asleep	☐ ....

CUBICLE ART

☐ Inside the box   ☐ Outside the box

ITEMS TAKEN DURING THIS VISIT:
- ☐ Stapler   ☐ Candy
- ☐ Scissors   ☐ Food
- ☐ Pens   ☐ Medication
- ☐ Toiletries   ☐ Valuables
- ☐ Gum   ☐ ....

ITEMS WERE:
- ☐ Given   ☐ "Borrowed"

TAKEAWAY FROM VISIT:
....
....

REPORT CARD	A	B	C	D	F
Ambience					
Cleanliness					
Décor					
Amenities					
Snacks					
Privacy					
Scuttlebutt					
OVERALL					

Memorable Moments: _____

_____

_____

_____

_____

Additional Sentiments: _____

_____

_____

_____

_____

Welcome to My Cubicle

DATE OF VISIT: ....

TIME OF VISIT: .... AM/PM

TV SHOW THAT BEST DESCRIBES THIS OFFICE:
- ☐ *Lost*
- ☐ *Survivor*
- ☐ *Mad Men*
- ☐ *Freaks and Geeks*
- ☐ *The A-Team*
- ☐ *Modern Family*
- ☐ ....

CUBICLE ACTIVITY BAR GRAPH
Shade in the amount of time spent doing the following:

NO TIME   LONG TIME

Liaising

Strategizing

Brainstorming

Procrastinating

Gossiping

SIGN IN, PLEASE

REASON FOR VISIT: ☐ Business   ☐ Pleasure   ☐ Boredom

HIDDEN AGENDA: ....

CUBICLE DWELLER WAS:	☐ At desk	☐ On coffee break	☐ Cubicle hopping
	☐ Out to lunch	☐ In meeting	☐ Who knows
	☐ In bathroom	☐ Asleep	☐ ....

CUBICLE ART

☐ Inside the box   ☐ Outside the box

ITEMS TAKEN DURING THIS VISIT:
- ☐ Stapler   ☐ Candy
- ☐ Scissors   ☐ Food
- ☐ Pens   ☐ Medication
- ☐ Toiletries   ☐ Valuables
- ☐ Gum   ☐ ....

ITEMS WERE:
- ☐ Given   ☐ "Borrowed"

TAKEAWAY FROM VISIT:
....
....

REPORT CARD	A	B	C	D	F
Ambience					
Cleanliness					
Décor					
Amenities					
Snacks					
Privacy					
Scuttlebutt					
OVERALL					

Memorable Moments: _____

_____

_____

_____

_____

Additional Sentiments: _____

_____

_____

_____

_____

Welcome to My Cubicle

DATE OF VISIT: ....

TIME OF VISIT: .... AM/PM

TV SHOW THAT BEST DESCRIBES THIS OFFICE:
- ☐ *Lost*
- ☐ *Survivor*
- ☐ *Mad Men*
- ☐ *Freaks and Geeks*
- ☐ *The A-Team*
- ☐ *Modern Family*
- ☐ ....

CUBICLE ACTIVITY BAR GRAPH
Shade in the amount of time spent doing the following:

NO TIME   LONG TIME

Liaising

Strategizing

Brainstorming

Procrastinating

Gossiping

SIGN IN, PLEASE

REASON FOR VISIT: ☐ Business ☐ Pleasure ☐ Boredom

HIDDEN AGENDA: ....

CUBICLE DWELLER WAS:
- ☐ At desk
- ☐ Out to lunch
- ☐ In bathroom
- ☐ On coffee break
- ☐ In meeting
- ☐ Asleep
- ☐ Cubicle hopping
- ☐ Who knows
- ☐ ....

CUBICLE ART

☐ Inside the box   ☐ Outside the box

ITEMS TAKEN DURING THIS VISIT:
- ☐ Stapler
- ☐ Scissors
- ☐ Pens
- ☐ Toiletries
- ☐ Gum
- ☐ Candy
- ☐ Food
- ☐ Medication
- ☐ Valuables
- ☐ ....

ITEMS WERE:
- ☐ Given
- ☐ "Borrowed"

TAKEAWAY FROM VISIT:
....
....

REPORT CARD	A	B	C	D	F
Ambience					
Cleanliness					
Décor					
Amenities					
Snacks					
Privacy					
Scuttlebutt					
OVERALL					

Memorable Moments: _____

_____

_____

_____

_____

_____

Additional Sentiments: _____

_____

_____

_____

_____

_____

Welcome to My Cubicle

DATE OF VISIT: ....

TIME OF VISIT: .... AM/PM

TV SHOW THAT BEST DESCRIBES THIS OFFICE:
- ☐ *Lost*
- ☐ *Survivor*
- ☐ *Mad Men*
- ☐ *Freaks and Geeks*
- ☐ *The A-Team*
- ☐ *Modern Family*
- ☐ ....

CUBICLE ACTIVITY BAR GRAPH
Shade in the amount of time spent doing the following:

	NO TIME	LONG TIME
Liaising		
Strategizing		
Brainstorming		
Procrastinating		
Gossiping		

SIGN IN, PLEASE

REASON FOR VISIT: ☐ Business ☐ Pleasure ☐ Boredom

HIDDEN AGENDA: ....

CUBICLE DWELLER WAS:
- ☐ At desk
- ☐ Out to lunch
- ☐ In bathroom
- ☐ On coffee break
- ☐ In meeting
- ☐ Asleep
- ☐ Cubicle hopping
- ☐ Who knows
- ☐ ....

CUBICLE ART

☐ Inside the box   ☐ Outside the box

ITEMS TAKEN DURING THIS VISIT:
- ☐ Stapler
- ☐ Scissors
- ☐ Pens
- ☐ Toiletries
- ☐ Gum
- ☐ Candy
- ☐ Food
- ☐ Medication
- ☐ Valuables
- ☐ ....

ITEMS WERE:
- ☐ Given
- ☐ "Borrowed"

TAKEAWAY FROM VISIT:
....
....

REPORT CARD	A	B	C	D	F
Ambience					
Cleanliness					
Décor					
Amenities					
Snacks					
Privacy					
Scuttlebutt					
OVERALL					

Memorable Moments: _____

_____

_____

_____

_____

_____

Additional Sentiments: _____

_____

_____

_____

_____

_____

Welcome to My Cubicle

DATE OF VISIT: ....

TIME OF VISIT: .... AM/PM

TV SHOW THAT BEST DESCRIBES THIS OFFICE:

- ☐ *Lost*
- ☐ *Survivor*
- ☐ *Mad Men*
- ☐ *Freaks and Geeks*
- ☐ *The A-Team*
- ☐ *Modern Family*
- ☐ ....

CUBICLE ACTIVITY BAR GRAPH

Shade in the amount of time spent doing the following:

	NO TIME	LONG TIME
Liaising		
Strategizing		
Brainstorming		
Procrastinating		
Gossiping		

SIGN IN, PLEASE

REASON FOR VISIT: ☐ Business ☐ Pleasure ☐ Boredom

HIDDEN AGENDA: ....

CUBICLE DWELLER WAS:	☐ At desk	☐ On coffee break	☐ Cubicle hopping
	☐ Out to lunch	☐ In meeting	☐ Who knows
	☐ In bathroom	☐ Asleep	☐ ....

CUBICLE ART

☐ Inside the box   ☐ Outside the box

ITEMS TAKEN DURING THIS VISIT:

- ☐ Stapler   ☐ Candy
- ☐ Scissors   ☐ Food
- ☐ Pens   ☐ Medication
- ☐ Toiletries ☐ Valuables
- ☐ Gum   ☐ ....

ITEMS WERE:

☐ Given   ☐ "Borrowed"

TAKEAWAY FROM VISIT:

....
....

REPORT CARD	A	B	C	D	F
Ambience					
Cleanliness					
Décor					
Amenities					
Snacks					
Privacy					
Scuttlebutt					
OVERALL					

Memorable Moments: _____

_____

_____

_____

_____

_____

Additional Sentiments: _____

_____

_____

_____

_____

_____

Welcome to My Cubicle

DATE OF VISIT: ....

TIME OF VISIT: .... AM/PM

TV SHOW THAT BEST DESCRIBES THIS OFFICE:
- ☐ *Lost*
- ☐ *Survivor*
- ☐ *Mad Men*
- ☐ *Freaks and Geeks*
- ☐ *The A-Team*
- ☐ *Modern Family*
- ☐ ....

CUBICLE ACTIVITY BAR GRAPH
Shade in the amount of time spent doing the following:

	NO TIME	LONG TIME
Liaising		
Strategizing		
Brainstorming		
Procrastinating		
Gossiping		

SIGN IN, PLEASE

REASON FOR VISIT: ☐ Business   ☐ Pleasure   ☐ Boredom

HIDDEN AGENDA: ....

CUBICLE DWELLER WAS:
- ☐ At desk
- ☐ Out to lunch
- ☐ In bathroom
- ☐ On coffee break
- ☐ In meeting
- ☐ Asleep
- ☐ Cubicle hopping
- ☐ Who knows
- ☐ ....

CUBICLE ART

☐ Inside the box   ☐ Outside the box

ITEMS TAKEN DURING THIS VISIT:
- ☐ Stapler
- ☐ Scissors
- ☐ Pens
- ☐ Toiletries
- ☐ Gum
- ☐ Candy
- ☐ Food
- ☐ Medication
- ☐ Valuables
- ☐ ....

ITEMS WERE:
- ☐ Given
- ☐ "Borrowed"

TAKEAWAY FROM VISIT:
....
....

REPORT CARD	A	B	C	D	F
Ambience					
Cleanliness					
Décor					
Amenities					
Snacks					
Privacy					
Scuttlebutt					
OVERALL					

Memorable Moments: _____
_____
_____
_____
_____
_____

Additional Sentiments: _____
_____
_____
_____
_____
_____

Welcome to My Cubicle

DATE OF VISIT: ....

TIME OF VISIT: .... AM/PM

TV SHOW THAT BEST DESCRIBES THIS OFFICE:
- ☐ Lost
- ☐ Survivor
- ☐ Mad Men
- ☐ Freaks and Geeks
- ☐ The A-Team
- ☐ Modern Family
- ☐ ....

CUBICLE ACTIVITY BAR GRAPH
Shade in the amount of time spent doing the following:

NO TIME   LONG TIME

Liaising

Strategizing

Brainstorming

Procrastinating

Gossiping

SIGN IN, PLEASE

REASON FOR VISIT: ☐ Business   ☐ Pleasure   ☐ Boredom

HIDDEN AGENDA: ....

CUBICLE DWELLER WAS:
- ☐ At desk
- ☐ Out to lunch
- ☐ In bathroom
- ☐ On coffee break
- ☐ In meeting
- ☐ Asleep
- ☐ Cubicle hopping
- ☐ Who knows
- ☐ ....

CUBICLE ART

☐ Inside the box   ☐ Outside the box

ITEMS TAKEN DURING THIS VISIT:
- ☐ Stapler
- ☐ Scissors
- ☐ Pens
- ☐ Toiletries
- ☐ Gum
- ☐ Candy
- ☐ Food
- ☐ Medication
- ☐ Valuables
- ☐ ....

ITEMS WERE:
- ☐ Given
- ☐ "Borrowed"

TAKEAWAY FROM VISIT:
....
....

REPORT CARD	A	B	C	D	F
Ambience					
Cleanliness					
Décor					
Amenities					
Snacks					
Privacy					
Scuttlebutt					
OVERALL					

Memorable Moments: _____

_____

_____

_____

_____

_____

Additional Sentiments: _____

_____

_____

_____

_____

_____

Welcome to My Cubicle

DATE OF VISIT: ....

TIME OF VISIT: .... AM/PM

TV SHOW THAT BEST DESCRIBES THIS OFFICE:
- ☐ *Lost*
- ☐ *Survivor*
- ☐ *Mad Men*
- ☐ *Freaks and Geeks*
- ☐ *The A-Team*
- ☐ *Modern Family*
- ☐ ....

CUBICLE ACTIVITY BAR GRAPH
Shade in the amount of time spent doing the following:

	NO TIME	LONG TIME
Liaising		
Strategizing		
Brainstorming		
Procrastinating		
Gossiping		

SIGN IN, PLEASE

REASON FOR VISIT: ☐ Business   ☐ Pleasure   ☐ Boredom

HIDDEN AGENDA: ....

CUBICLE DWELLER WAS:
- ☐ At desk
- ☐ Out to lunch
- ☐ In bathroom
- ☐ On coffee break
- ☐ In meeting
- ☐ Asleep
- ☐ Cubicle hopping
- ☐ Who knows
- ☐ ....

CUBICLE ART

☐ Inside the box   ☐ Outside the box

ITEMS TAKEN DURING THIS VISIT:
- ☐ Stapler
- ☐ Scissors
- ☐ Pens
- ☐ Toiletries
- ☐ Gum
- ☐ Candy
- ☐ Food
- ☐ Medication
- ☐ Valuables
- ☐ ....

ITEMS WERE:
- ☐ Given
- ☐ "Borrowed"

TAKEAWAY FROM VISIT:
....
....

REPORT CARD	A	B	C	D	F
Ambience					
Cleanliness					
Décor					
Amenities					
Snacks					
Privacy					
Scuttlebutt					
OVERALL					

Memorable Moments: _____

_____

_____

_____

_____

Additional Sentiments: _____

_____

_____

_____

_____

Welcome to My Cubicle

DATE OF VISIT: ....

TIME OF VISIT: .... AM/PM

TV SHOW THAT BEST DESCRIBES THIS OFFICE:
- ☐ *Lost*
- ☐ *Survivor*
- ☐ *Mad Men*
- ☐ *Freaks and Geeks*
- ☐ *The A-Team*
- ☐ *Modern Family*
- ☐ ....

CUBICLE ACTIVITY BAR GRAPH
Shade in the amount of time spent doing the following:

NO TIME   LONG TIME

Liaising

Strategizing

Brainstorming

Procrastinating

Gossiping

SIGN IN, PLEASE

REASON FOR VISIT: ☐ Business   ☐ Pleasure   ☐ Boredom

HIDDEN AGENDA: ....

CUBICLE DWELLER WAS:
- ☐ At desk
- ☐ Out to lunch
- ☐ In bathroom
- ☐ On coffee break
- ☐ In meeting
- ☐ Asleep
- ☐ Cubicle hopping
- ☐ Who knows
- ☐ ....

CUBICLE ART

☐ Inside the box   ☐ Outside the box

ITEMS TAKEN DURING THIS VISIT:
- ☐ Stapler
- ☐ Scissors
- ☐ Pens
- ☐ Toiletries
- ☐ Gum
- ☐ Candy
- ☐ Food
- ☐ Medication
- ☐ Valuables
- ☐ ....

ITEMS WERE:
- ☐ Given
- ☐ "Borrowed"

TAKEAWAY FROM VISIT:
....
....

REPORT CARD	A	B	C	D	F
Ambience					
Cleanliness					
Décor					
Amenities					
Snacks					
Privacy					
Scuttlebutt					
OVERALL					

Memorable Moments: _____

_____

_____

_____

_____

_____

Additional Sentiments: _____

_____

_____

_____

_____

_____

Welcome to My Cubicle

DATE OF VISIT: ....

TIME OF VISIT: .... AM/PM

TV SHOW THAT BEST DESCRIBES THIS OFFICE:
- ☐ *Lost*
- ☐ *Survivor*
- ☐ *Mad Men*
- ☐ *Freaks and Geeks*
- ☐ *The A-Team*
- ☐ *Modern Family*
- ☐ ....

CUBICLE ACTIVITY BAR GRAPH
Shade in the amount of time spent doing the following:

NO TIME   LONG TIME

Liaising

Strategizing

Brainstorming

Procrastinating

Gossiping

SIGN IN, PLEASE

REASON FOR VISIT: ☐ Business   ☐ Pleasure   ☐ Boredom

HIDDEN AGENDA: ....

CUBICLE DWELLER WAS:	☐ At desk	☐ On coffee break	☐ Cubicle hopping
	☐ Out to lunch	☐ In meeting	☐ Who knows
	☐ In bathroom	☐ Asleep	☐ ....

CUBICLE ART

☐ Inside the box   ☐ Outside the box

ITEMS TAKEN DURING THIS VISIT:
- ☐ Stapler   ☐ Candy
- ☐ Scissors   ☐ Food
- ☐ Pens   ☐ Medication
- ☐ Toiletries   ☐ Valuables
- ☐ Gum   ☐ ....

ITEMS WERE:
- ☐ Given   ☐ "Borrowed"

TAKEAWAY FROM VISIT:
....
....

REPORT CARD	A	B	C	D	F
Ambience					
Cleanliness					
Décor					
Amenities					
Snacks					
Privacy					
Scuttlebutt					
OVERALL					

Memorable Moments: _____

_____

_____

_____

_____

_____

Additional Sentiments: _____

_____

_____

_____

_____

_____

Welcome to My Cubicle

DATE OF VISIT: ....

TIME OF VISIT: .... AM/PM

TV SHOW THAT BEST DESCRIBES THIS OFFICE:

☐ *Lost*
☐ *Survivor*
☐ *Mad Men*
☐ *Freaks and Geeks*
☐ *The A-Team*
☐ *Modern Family*
☐ ....

CUBICLE ACTIVITY BAR GRAPH
Shade in the amount of time spent doing the following:

NO TIME   LONG TIME

Liaising

Strategizing

Brainstorming

Procrastinating

Gossiping

SIGN IN, PLEASE

REASON FOR VISIT: ☐ Business   ☐ Pleasure   ☐ Boredom

HIDDEN AGENDA: ....

CUBICLE DWELLER WAS:	☐ At desk	☐ On coffee break	☐ Cubicle hopping
	☐ Out to lunch	☐ In meeting	☐ Who knows
	☐ In bathroom	☐ Asleep	☐ ....

CUBICLE ART

☐ Inside the box   ☐ Outside the box

ITEMS TAKEN DURING THIS VISIT:

☐ Stapler   ☐ Candy
☐ Scissors   ☐ Food
☐ Pens   ☐ Medication
☐ Toiletries   ☐ Valuables
☐ Gum   ☐ ....

ITEMS WERE:

☐ Given   ☐ "Borrowed"

TAKEAWAY FROM VISIT:

....
....

REPORT CARD	A	B	C	D	F
Ambience					
Cleanliness					
Décor					
Amenities					
Snacks					
Privacy					
Scuttlebutt					
OVERALL					

Memorable Moments: _____

_____

_____

_____

_____

_____

Additional Sentiments: _____

_____

_____

_____

_____

_____

Welcome to My Cubicle

DATE OF VISIT: ....

TIME OF VISIT: .... AM/PM

TV SHOW THAT BEST DESCRIBES THIS OFFICE:

- ☐ *Lost*
- ☐ *Survivor*
- ☐ *Mad Men*
- ☐ *Freaks and Geeks*
- ☐ *The A-Team*
- ☐ *Modern Family*
- ☐ ....

CUBICLE ACTIVITY BAR GRAPH

Shade in the amount of time spent doing the following:

	NO TIME	LONG TIME
Liaising		
Strategizing		
Brainstorming		
Procrastinating		
Gossiping		

SIGN IN, PLEASE

REASON FOR VISIT: ☐ Business   ☐ Pleasure   ☐ Boredom

HIDDEN AGENDA: ....

CUBICLE DWELLER WAS:	☐ At desk	☐ On coffee break	☐ Cubicle hopping
	☐ Out to lunch	☐ In meeting	☐ Who knows
	☐ In bathroom	☐ Asleep	☐ ....

CUBICLE ART

☐ Inside the box   ☐ Outside the box

ITEMS TAKEN DURING THIS VISIT:

- ☐ Stapler ☐ Candy
- ☐ Scissors ☐ Food
- ☐ Pens ☐ Medication
- ☐ Toiletries ☐ Valuables
- ☐ Gum ☐ ....

ITEMS WERE:

☐ Given   ☐ "Borrowed"

TAKEAWAY FROM VISIT:
....
....

REPORT CARD	A	B	C	D	F
Ambience					
Cleanliness					
Décor					
Amenities					
Snacks					
Privacy					
Scuttlebutt					
OVERALL					

Memorable Moments: _____

_____

_____

_____

_____

_____

Additional Sentiments: _____

_____

_____

_____

_____

_____

Welcome to My Cubicle

DATE OF VISIT: ....

TIME OF VISIT: .... AM/PM

TV SHOW THAT BEST DESCRIBES THIS OFFICE:

- ☐ *Lost*
- ☐ *Survivor*
- ☐ *Mad Men*
- ☐ *Freaks and Geeks*
- ☐ *The A-Team*
- ☐ *Modern Family*
- ☐ ....

CUBICLE ACTIVITY BAR GRAPH

Shade in the amount of time spent doing the following:

	NO TIME	LONG TIME
Liaising		
Strategizing		
Brainstorming		
Procrastinating		
Gossiping		

SIGN IN, PLEASE

REASON FOR VISIT: ☐ Business   ☐ Pleasure   ☐ Boredom

HIDDEN AGENDA: ....

CUBICLE DWELLER WAS:
- ☐ At desk
- ☐ Out to lunch
- ☐ In bathroom
- ☐ On coffee break
- ☐ In meeting
- ☐ Asleep
- ☐ Cubicle hopping
- ☐ Who knows
- ☐ ....

CUBICLE ART

☐ Inside the box   ☐ Outside the box

ITEMS TAKEN DURING THIS VISIT:

- ☐ Stapler
- ☐ Scissors
- ☐ Pens
- ☐ Toiletries
- ☐ Gum
- ☐ Candy
- ☐ Food
- ☐ Medication
- ☐ Valuables
- ☐ ....

ITEMS WERE:

- ☐ Given
- ☐ "Borrowed"

TAKEAWAY FROM VISIT:
....
....

REPORT CARD	A	B	C	D	F
Ambience					
Cleanliness					
Décor					
Amenities					
Snacks					
Privacy					
Scuttlebutt					
OVERALL					

Memorable Moments: _____

_____
_____
_____
_____
_____

Additional Sentiments: _____

_____
_____
_____
_____
_____

Welcome to My Cubicle

DATE OF VISIT: ....

TIME OF VISIT: .... AM/PM

TV SHOW THAT BEST DESCRIBES THIS OFFICE:
- ☐ *Lost*
- ☐ *Survivor*
- ☐ *Mad Men*
- ☐ *Freaks and Geeks*
- ☐ *The A-Team*
- ☐ *Modern Family*
- ☐ ....

CUBICLE ACTIVITY BAR GRAPH
Shade in the amount of time spent doing the following:

NO TIME   LONG TIME

Liaising

Strategizing

Brainstorming

Procrastinating

Gossiping

SIGN IN, PLEASE

REASON FOR VISIT: ☐ Business   ☐ Pleasure   ☐ Boredom

HIDDEN AGENDA: ....

CUBICLE DWELLER WAS:	☐ At desk	☐ On coffee break	☐ Cubicle hopping
	☐ Out to lunch	☐ In meeting	☐ Who knows
	☐ In bathroom	☐ Asleep	☐ ....

CUBICLE ART

☐ Inside the box   ☐ Outside the box

ITEMS TAKEN DURING THIS VISIT:
- ☐ Stapler
- ☐ Scissors
- ☐ Pens
- ☐ Toiletries
- ☐ Gum
- ☐ Candy
- ☐ Food
- ☐ Medication
- ☐ Valuables
- ☐ ....

ITEMS WERE:
- ☐ Given
- ☐ "Borrowed"

TAKEAWAY FROM VISIT:
....
....

REPORT CARD	A	B	C	D	F
Ambience					
Cleanliness					
Décor					
Amenities					
Snacks					
Privacy					
Scuttlebutt					
OVERALL					

Memorable Moments: _____

_____

_____

_____

_____

_____

Additional Sentiments: _____

_____

_____

_____

_____

Welcome to My Cubicle

DATE OF VISIT: ....

TIME OF VISIT: .... AM/PM

TV SHOW THAT BEST DESCRIBES THIS OFFICE:

☐ *Lost*
☐ *Survivor*
☐ *Mad Men*
☐ *Freaks and Geeks*
☐ *The A-Team*
☐ *Modern Family*
☐ ....

CUBICLE ACTIVITY BAR GRAPH

Shade in the amount of time spent doing the following:

	NO TIME	LONG TIME

Liaising

Strategizing

Brainstorming

Procrastinating

Gossiping

SIGN IN, PLEASE

REASON FOR VISIT: ☐ Business ☐ Pleasure ☐ Boredom

HIDDEN AGENDA: ....

CUBICLE DWELLER WAS:	☐ At desk	☐ On coffee break	☐ Cubicle hopping
	☐ Out to lunch	☐ In meeting	☐ Who knows
	☐ In bathroom	☐ Asleep	☐ ....

CUBICLE ART

☐ Inside the box   ☐ Outside the box

ITEMS TAKEN DURING THIS VISIT:

☐ Stapler   ☐ Candy
☐ Scissors   ☐ Food
☐ Pens   ☐ Medication
☐ Toiletries ☐ Valuables
☐ Gum   ☐ ....

ITEMS WERE:

☐ Given   ☐ "Borrowed"

TAKEAWAY FROM VISIT:

....
....

REPORT CARD	A	B	C	D	F
Ambience					
Cleanliness					
Décor					
Amenities					
Snacks					
Privacy					
Scuttlebutt					
OVERALL					

Memorable Moments: _____

_____

_____

_____

_____

_____

Additional Sentiments: _____

_____

_____

_____

_____

Welcome to My Cubicle

DATE OF VISIT: ....

TIME OF VISIT: .... AM/PM

TV SHOW THAT BEST DESCRIBES THIS OFFICE:
- ☐ *Lost*
- ☐ *Survivor*
- ☐ *Mad Men*
- ☐ *Freaks and Geeks*
- ☐ *The A-Team*
- ☐ *Modern Family*
- ☐ ....

CUBICLE ACTIVITY BAR GRAPH
Shade in the amount of time spent doing the following:

	NO TIME	LONG TIME
Liaising		
Strategizing		
Brainstorming		
Procrastinating		
Gossiping		

SIGN IN, PLEASE

REASON FOR VISIT: ☐ Business ☐ Pleasure ☐ Boredom

HIDDEN AGENDA: ....

CUBICLE DWELLER WAS:	☐ At desk	☐ On coffee break	☐ Cubicle hopping
	☐ Out to lunch	☐ In meeting	☐ Who knows
	☐ In bathroom	☐ Asleep	☐ ....

CUBICLE ART

☐ Inside the box   ☐ Outside the box

ITEMS TAKEN DURING THIS VISIT:
- ☐ Stapler   ☐ Candy
- ☐ Scissors   ☐ Food
- ☐ Pens   ☐ Medication
- ☐ Toiletries   ☐ Valuables
- ☐ Gum   ☐ ....

ITEMS WERE:
☐ Given   ☐ "Borrowed"

TAKEAWAY FROM VISIT:
....
....

REPORT CARD	A	B	C	D	F
Ambience					
Cleanliness					
Décor					
Amenities					
Snacks					
Privacy					
Scuttlebutt					
OVERALL					

Memorable Moments: _____

_____
_____
_____
_____
_____

Additional Sentiments: _____

_____
_____
_____
_____
_____

Welcome to My Cubicle

DATE OF VISIT: ....

TIME OF VISIT: .... AM/PM

TV SHOW THAT BEST DESCRIBES THIS OFFICE:
- ☐ *Lost*
- ☐ *Survivor*
- ☐ *Mad Men*
- ☐ *Freaks and Geeks*
- ☐ *The A-Team*
- ☐ *Modern Family*
- ☐

CUBICLE ACTIVITY BAR GRAPH
Shade in the amount of time spent doing the following:

NO TIME   LONG TIME

Liaising

Strategizing

Brainstorming

Procrastinating

Gossiping

SIGN IN, PLEASE

REASON FOR VISIT: ☐ Business   ☐ Pleasure   ☐ Boredom

HIDDEN AGENDA: ....

CUBICLE DWELLER WAS:	☐ At desk	☐ On coffee break	☐ Cubicle hopping
	☐ Out to lunch	☐ In meeting	☐ Who knows
	☐ In bathroom	☐ Asleep	☐ ....

CUBICLE ART

☐ Inside the box   ☐ Outside the box

ITEMS TAKEN DURING THIS VISIT:
- ☐ Stapler   ☐ Candy
- ☐ Scissors   ☐ Food
- ☐ Pens   ☐ Medication
- ☐ Toiletries   ☐ Valuables
- ☐ Gum   ☐ ....

ITEMS WERE:
- ☐ Given   ☐ "Borrowed"

TAKEAWAY FROM VISIT:
....
....

REPORT CARD	A	B	C	D	F
Ambience					
Cleanliness					
Décor					
Amenities					
Snacks					
Privacy					
Scuttlebutt					
OVERALL					

Memorable Moments: _____

_____

_____

_____

_____

_____

Additional Sentiments: _____

_____

_____

_____

_____

_____

Welcome to My Cubicle

DATE OF VISIT: ....

TIME OF VISIT: .... AM/PM

TV SHOW THAT BEST DESCRIBES THIS OFFICE:
- ☐ *Lost*
- ☐ *Survivor*
- ☐ *Mad Men*
- ☐ *Freaks and Geeks*
- ☐ *The A-Team*
- ☐ *Modern Family*
- ☐

CUBICLE ACTIVITY BAR GRAPH
Shade in the amount of time spent doing the following:

	NO TIME	LONG TIME
Liaising		
Strategizing		
Brainstorming		
Procrastinating		
Gossiping		

SIGN IN, PLEASE

REASON FOR VISIT: ☐ Business   ☐ Pleasure   ☐ Boredom

HIDDEN AGENDA: ....

CUBICLE DWELLER WAS:
- ☐ At desk
- ☐ Out to lunch
- ☐ In bathroom
- ☐ On coffee break
- ☐ In meeting
- ☐ Asleep
- ☐ Cubicle hopping
- ☐ Who knows
- ☐ ....

CUBICLE ART

☐ Inside the box   ☐ Outside the box

ITEMS TAKEN DURING THIS VISIT:
- ☐ Stapler
- ☐ Scissors
- ☐ Pens
- ☐ Toiletries
- ☐ Gum
- ☐ Candy
- ☐ Food
- ☐ Medication
- ☐ Valuables
- ☐ ....

ITEMS WERE:
- ☐ Given
- ☐ "Borrowed"

TAKEAWAY FROM VISIT:
....
....

REPORT CARD	A	B	C	D	F
Ambience					
Cleanliness					
Décor					
Amenities					
Snacks					
Privacy					
Scuttlebutt					
OVERALL					

Memorable Moments: _____
_____
_____
_____
_____
_____

Additional Sentiments: _____
_____
_____
_____
_____
_____

Welcome to My Cubicle

DATE OF VISIT: ....

TIME OF VISIT: .... AM/PM

TV SHOW THAT BEST DESCRIBES THIS OFFICE:

☐ *Lost*
☐ *Survivor*
☐ *Mad Men*
☐ *Freaks and Geeks*
☐ *The A-Team*
☐ *Modern Family*
☐ ....

CUBICLE ACTIVITY BAR GRAPH

Shade in the amount of time spent doing the following:

	NO TIME	LONG TIME

Liaising

Strategizing

Brainstorming

Procrastinating

Gossiping

SIGN IN, PLEASE

REASON FOR VISIT: ☐ Business   ☐ Pleasure   ☐ Boredom

HIDDEN AGENDA: ....

CUBICLE DWELLER WAS:	☐ At desk	☐ On coffee break	☐ Cubicle hopping
	☐ Out to lunch	☐ In meeting	☐ Who knows
	☐ In bathroom	☐ Asleep	☐ ....

CUBICLE ART

☐ Inside the box   ☐ Outside the box

ITEMS TAKEN DURING THIS VISIT:

☐ Stapler   ☐ Candy
☐ Scissors   ☐ Food
☐ Pens   ☐ Medication
☐ Toiletries   ☐ Valuables
☐ Gum   ☐ ....

ITEMS WERE:

☐ Given   ☐ "Borrowed"

TAKEAWAY FROM VISIT:
....
....

REPORT CARD	A	B	C	D	F
Ambience					
Cleanliness					
Décor					
Amenities					
Snacks					
Privacy					
Scuttlebutt					
OVERALL					

Memorable Moments: _____

_____

_____

_____

_____

_____

Additional Sentiments: _____

_____

_____

_____

_____

_____

Welcome to My Cubicle

DATE OF VISIT: ....

TIME OF VISIT: .... AM/PM

TV SHOW THAT BEST DESCRIBES THIS OFFICE:

- ☐ *Lost*
- ☐ *Survivor*
- ☐ *Mad Men*
- ☐ *Freaks and Geeks*
- ☐ *The A-Team*
- ☐ *Modern Family*
- ☐ ....

CUBICLE ACTIVITY BAR GRAPH

Shade in the amount of time spent doing the following:

	NO TIME	LONG TIME

Liaising

Strategizing

Brainstorming

Procrastinating

Gossiping

SIGN IN, PLEASE

REASON FOR VISIT: ☐ Business   ☐ Pleasure   ☐ Boredom

HIDDEN AGENDA: ....

CUBICLE DWELLER WAS:
- ☐ At desk
- ☐ Out to lunch
- ☐ In bathroom
- ☐ On coffee break
- ☐ In meeting
- ☐ Asleep
- ☐ Cubicle hopping
- ☐ Who knows
- ☐ ....

CUBICLE ART

☐ Inside the box   ☐ Outside the box

ITEMS TAKEN DURING THIS VISIT:

- ☐ Stapler
- ☐ Scissors
- ☐ Pens
- ☐ Toiletries
- ☐ Gum
- ☐ Candy
- ☐ Food
- ☐ Medication
- ☐ Valuables
- ☐ ....

ITEMS WERE:

☐ Given   ☐ "Borrowed"

TAKEAWAY FROM VISIT:

....
....

REPORT CARD	A	B	C	D	F
Ambience					
Cleanliness					
Décor					
Amenities					
Snacks					
Privacy					
Scuttlebutt					
OVERALL					

Memorable Moments: _____

_____

_____

_____

_____

_____

Additional Sentiments: _____

_____

_____

_____

_____

_____

Welcome to My Cubicle

DATE OF VISIT: ....

TIME OF VISIT: .... AM/PM

TV SHOW THAT BEST DESCRIBES THIS OFFICE:
- ☐ *Lost*
- ☐ *Survivor*
- ☐ *Mad Men*
- ☐ *Freaks and Geeks*
- ☐ *The A-Team*
- ☐ *Modern Family*
- ☐ ....

CUBICLE ACTIVITY BAR GRAPH

Shade in the amount of time spent doing the following:

	NO TIME	LONG TIME
Liaising		
Strategizing		
Brainstorming		
Procrastinating		
Gossiping		

SIGN IN, PLEASE

REASON FOR VISIT: ☐ Business   ☐ Pleasure   ☐ Boredom

HIDDEN AGENDA: ....

CUBICLE DWELLER WAS:	☐ At desk	☐ On coffee break	☐ Cubicle hopping
	☐ Out to lunch	☐ In meeting	☐ Who knows
	☐ In bathroom	☐ Asleep	☐ ....

CUBICLE ART

☐ Inside the box   ☐ Outside the box

ITEMS TAKEN DURING THIS VISIT:
- ☐ Stapler
- ☐ Scissors
- ☐ Pens
- ☐ Toiletries
- ☐ Gum
- ☐ Candy
- ☐ Food
- ☐ Medication
- ☐ Valuables
- ☐ ....

ITEMS WERE:
- ☐ Given
- ☐ "Borrowed"

TAKEAWAY FROM VISIT:
....
....

REPORT CARD	A	B	C	D	F
Ambience					
Cleanliness					
Décor					
Amenities					
Snacks					
Privacy					
Scuttlebutt					
OVERALL					

Memorable Moments: _____

_____

_____

_____

_____

_____

Additional Sentiments: _____

_____

_____

_____

_____

_____

Welcome to My Cubicle

DATE OF VISIT: ....

TIME OF VISIT: .... AM/PM

TV SHOW THAT BEST DESCRIBES THIS OFFICE:

- ☐ *Lost*
- ☐ *Survivor*
- ☐ *Mad Men*
- ☐ *Freaks and Geeks*
- ☐ *The A-Team*
- ☐ *Modern Family*
- ☐ ....

CUBICLE ACTIVITY BAR GRAPH

Shade in the amount of time spent doing the following:

NO TIME   LONG TIME

Liaising

Strategizing

Brainstorming

Procrastinating

Gossiping

SIGN IN, PLEASE

REASON FOR VISIT: ☐ Business   ☐ Pleasure   ☐ Boredom

HIDDEN AGENDA: ....

CUBICLE DWELLER WAS:
- ☐ At desk
- ☐ Out to lunch
- ☐ In bathroom
- ☐ On coffee break
- ☐ In meeting
- ☐ Asleep
- ☐ Cubicle hopping
- ☐ Who knows
- ☐ ....

CUBICLE ART

☐ Inside the box   ☐ Outside the box

ITEMS TAKEN DURING THIS VISIT:

- ☐ Stapler
- ☐ Scissors
- ☐ Pens
- ☐ Toiletries
- ☐ Gum
- ☐ Candy
- ☐ Food
- ☐ Medication
- ☐ Valuables
- ☐ ....

ITEMS WERE:

- ☐ Given
- ☐ "Borrowed"

TAKEAWAY FROM VISIT:
....
....

REPORT CARD	A	B	C	D	F
Ambience					
Cleanliness					
Décor					
Amenities					
Snacks					
Privacy					
Scuttlebutt					
OVERALL					

Memorable Moments: _____
_____
_____
_____
_____
_____

Additional Sentiments: _____
_____
_____
_____
_____
_____

Welcome to My Cubicle

DATE OF VISIT: ....

TIME OF VISIT: .... AM/PM

TV SHOW THAT BEST DESCRIBES THIS OFFICE:

- ☐ *Lost*
- ☐ *Survivor*
- ☐ *Mad Men*
- ☐ *Freaks and Geeks*
- ☐ *The A-Team*
- ☐ *Modern Family*
- ☐ ....

CUBICLE ACTIVITY BAR GRAPH

Shade in the amount of time spent doing the following:

NO TIME   LONG TIME

Liaising

Strategizing

Brainstorming

Procrastinating

Gossiping

SIGN IN, PLEASE

REASON FOR VISIT: ☐ Business   ☐ Pleasure   ☐ Boredom

HIDDEN AGENDA: ....

CUBICLE DWELLER WAS:	☐ At desk	☐ On coffee break	☐ Cubicle hopping
	☐ Out to lunch	☐ In meeting	☐ Who knows
	☐ In bathroom	☐ Asleep	☐ ....

CUBICLE ART

☐ Inside the box   ☐ Outside the box

ITEMS TAKEN DURING THIS VISIT:

- ☐ Stapler   ☐ Candy
- ☐ Scissors   ☐ Food
- ☐ Pens   ☐ Medication
- ☐ Toiletries   ☐ Valuables
- ☐ Gum   ☐ ....

ITEMS WERE:

☐ Given   ☐ "Borrowed"

TAKEAWAY FROM VISIT:

....
....

REPORT CARD	A	B	C	D	F
Ambience					
Cleanliness					
Décor					
Amenities					
Snacks					
Privacy					
Scuttlebutt					
OVERALL					

Memorable Moments: _____

_____

_____

_____

_____

Additional Sentiments: _____

_____

_____

_____

_____

Welcome to My Cubicle

DATE OF VISIT: ....

TIME OF VISIT: .... AM/PM

TV SHOW THAT BEST DESCRIBES THIS OFFICE:
☐ Lost
☐ Survivor
☐ Mad Men
☐ Freaks and Geeks
☐ The A-Team
☐ Modern Family
☐ ....

CUBICLE ACTIVITY BAR GRAPH
Shade in the amount of time spent doing the following:

	NO TIME	LONG TIME

Liaising

Strategizing

Brainstorming

Procrastinating

Gossiping

SIGN IN, PLEASE

REASON FOR VISIT: ☐ Business ☐ Pleasure ☐ Boredom

HIDDEN AGENDA: ....

CUBICLE DWELLER WAS:	☐ At desk	☐ On coffee break	☐ Cubicle hopping
	☐ Out to lunch	☐ In meeting	☐ Who knows
	☐ In bathroom	☐ Asleep	☐ ....

CUBICLE ART

☐ Inside the box   ☐ Outside the box

ITEMS TAKEN DURING THIS VISIT:
☐ Stapler   ☐ Candy
☐ Scissors   ☐ Food
☐ Pens   ☐ Medication
☐ Toiletries   ☐ Valuables
☐ Gum   ☐ ....

ITEMS WERE:
☐ Given   ☐ "Borrowed"

TAKEAWAY FROM VISIT:
....
....

REPORT CARD	A	B	C	D	F
Ambience					
Cleanliness					
Décor					
Amenities					
Snacks					
Privacy					
Scuttlebutt					
OVERALL					

Memorable Moments: _____

_____

_____

_____

_____

_____

Additional Sentiments: _____

_____

_____

_____

_____

_____

Welcome to My Cubicle

DATE OF VISIT: ....

TIME OF VISIT: .... AM/PM

TV SHOW THAT BEST DESCRIBES THIS OFFICE:

- ☐ *Lost*
- ☐ *Survivor*
- ☐ *Mad Men*
- ☐ *Freaks and Geeks*
- ☐ *The A-Team*
- ☐ *Modern Family*
- ☐ ....

CUBICLE ACTIVITY BAR GRAPH

Shade in the amount of time spent doing the following:

	NO TIME	LONG TIME
Liaising		
Strategizing		
Brainstorming		
Procrastinating		
Gossiping		

SIGN IN, PLEASE

REASON FOR VISIT: ☐ Business   ☐ Pleasure   ☐ Boredom

HIDDEN AGENDA: ....

CUBICLE DWELLER WAS:	☐ At desk	☐ On coffee break	☐ Cubicle hopping
	☐ Out to lunch	☐ In meeting	☐ Who knows
	☐ In bathroom	☐ Asleep	☐ ....

CUBICLE ART

☐ Inside the box   ☐ Outside the box

ITEMS TAKEN DURING THIS VISIT:

- ☐ Stapler
- ☐ Scissors
- ☐ Pens
- ☐ Toiletries
- ☐ Gum
- ☐ Candy
- ☐ Food
- ☐ Medication
- ☐ Valuables
- ☐ ....

ITEMS WERE:

☐ Given   ☐ "Borrowed"

TAKEAWAY FROM VISIT:
....
....

REPORT CARD	A	B	C	D	F
Ambience					
Cleanliness					
Décor					
Amenities					
Snacks					
Privacy					
Scuttlebutt					
OVERALL					

Memorable Moments: _____

_____

_____

_____

_____

_____

Additional Sentiments: _____

_____

_____

_____

_____

Welcome to My Cubicle

DATE OF VISIT: ....

TIME OF VISIT: .... AM/PM

TV SHOW THAT BEST DESCRIBES THIS OFFICE:
- ☐ *Lost*
- ☐ *Survivor*
- ☐ *Mad Men*
- ☐ *Freaks and Geeks*
- ☐ *The A-Team*
- ☐ *Modern Family*
- ☐ ....

CUBICLE ACTIVITY BAR GRAPH
Shade in the amount of time spent doing the following:

	NO TIME	LONG TIME

Liaising

Strategizing

Brainstorming

Procrastinating

Gossiping

SIGN IN, PLEASE

REASON FOR VISIT: ☐ Business ☐ Pleasure ☐ Boredom

HIDDEN AGENDA: ....

CUBICLE DWELLER WAS:	☐ At desk	☐ On coffee break	☐ Cubicle hopping
	☐ Out to lunch	☐ In meeting	☐ Who knows
	☐ In bathroom	☐ Asleep	☐ ....

CUBICLE ART

☐ Inside the box   ☐ Outside the box

ITEMS TAKEN DURING THIS VISIT:
- ☐ Stapler
- ☐ Scissors
- ☐ Pens
- ☐ Toiletries
- ☐ Gum
- ☐ Candy
- ☐ Food
- ☐ Medication
- ☐ Valuables
- ☐ ....

ITEMS WERE:
☐ Given   ☐ "Borrowed"

TAKEAWAY FROM VISIT:
....
....

REPORT CARD	A	B	C	D	F
Ambience					
Cleanliness					
Décor					
Amenities					
Snacks					
Privacy					
Scuttlebutt					
OVERALL					

Memorable Moments: _____

_____

_____

_____

_____

_____

Additional Sentiments: _____

_____

_____

_____

_____

_____

Welcome to My Cubicle

DATE OF VISIT: ....

TIME OF VISIT: .... AM/PM

TV SHOW THAT BEST DESCRIBES THIS OFFICE:

- ☐ Lost
- ☐ Survivor
- ☐ Mad Men
- ☐ Freaks and Geeks
- ☐ The A-Team
- ☐ Modern Family
- ☐

CUBICLE ACTIVITY BAR GRAPH

Shade in the amount of time spent doing the following:

	NO TIME	LONG TIME
Liaising		
Strategizing		
Brainstorming		
Procrastinating		
Gossiping		

SIGN IN, PLEASE

REASON FOR VISIT: ☐ Business ☐ Pleasure ☐ Boredom

HIDDEN AGENDA: ....

CUBICLE DWELLER WAS:	☐ At desk	☐ On coffee break	☐ Cubicle hopping
	☐ Out to lunch	☐ In meeting	☐ Who knows
	☐ In bathroom	☐ Asleep	☐ ....

CUBICLE ART

☐ Inside the box   ☐ Outside the box

ITEMS TAKEN DURING THIS VISIT:

- ☐ Stapler
- ☐ Scissors
- ☐ Pens
- ☐ Toiletries
- ☐ Gum
- ☐ Candy
- ☐ Food
- ☐ Medication
- ☐ Valuables
- ☐

ITEMS WERE:

☐ Given   ☐ "Borrowed"

TAKEAWAY FROM VISIT:
....
....

REPORT CARD	A	B	C	D	F
Ambience					
Cleanliness					
Décor					
Amenities					
Snacks					
Privacy					
Scuttlebutt					
OVERALL					

Memorable Moments: _____

_____

_____

_____

_____

Additional Sentiments: _____

_____

_____

_____

_____

Welcome to My Cubicle

DATE OF VISIT: ....

TIME OF VISIT: .... AM/PM

TV SHOW THAT BEST DESCRIBES THIS OFFICE:
- ☐ *Lost*
- ☐ *Survivor*
- ☐ *Mad Men*
- ☐ *Freaks and Geeks*
- ☐ *The A-Team*
- ☐ *Modern Family*
- ☐ ....

CUBICLE ACTIVITY BAR GRAPH
Shade in the amount of time spent doing the following:

NO TIME   LONG TIME

Liaising

Strategizing

Brainstorming

Procrastinating

Gossiping

SIGN IN, PLEASE

REASON FOR VISIT: ☐ Business   ☐ Pleasure   ☐ Boredom

HIDDEN AGENDA: ....

CUBICLE DWELLER WAS:
- ☐ At desk
- ☐ Out to lunch
- ☐ In bathroom
- ☐ On coffee break
- ☐ In meeting
- ☐ Asleep
- ☐ Cubicle hopping
- ☐ Who knows
- ☐ ....

CUBICLE ART

☐ Inside the box   ☐ Outside the box

ITEMS TAKEN DURING THIS VISIT:
- ☐ Stapler
- ☐ Scissors
- ☐ Pens
- ☐ Toiletries
- ☐ Gum
- ☐ Candy
- ☐ Food
- ☐ Medication
- ☐ Valuables
- ☐ ....

ITEMS WERE:
- ☐ Given
- ☐ "Borrowed"

TAKEAWAY FROM VISIT:
....
....

REPORT CARD	A	B	C	D	F
Ambience					
Cleanliness					
Décor					
Amenities					
Snacks					
Privacy					
Scuttlebutt					
OVERALL					

Memorable Moments: _____
_____
_____
_____
_____
_____

Additional Sentiments: _____
_____
_____
_____
_____
_____

Welcome to My Cubicle

DATE OF VISIT: ....

TIME OF VISIT: .... AM/PM

TV SHOW THAT BEST DESCRIBES THIS OFFICE:

- ☐ *Lost*
- ☐ *Survivor*
- ☐ *Mad Men*
- ☐ *Freaks and Geeks*
- ☐ *The A-Team*
- ☐ *Modern Family*
- ☐ ....

CUBICLE ACTIVITY BAR GRAPH

Shade in the amount of time spent doing the following:

	NO TIME	LONG TIME
Liaising		
Strategizing		
Brainstorming		
Procrastinating		
Gossiping		

SIGN IN, PLEASE

REASON FOR VISIT: ☐ Business   ☐ Pleasure   ☐ Boredom

HIDDEN AGENDA: ....

CUBICLE DWELLER WAS:
- ☐ At desk
- ☐ Out to lunch
- ☐ In bathroom
- ☐ On coffee break
- ☐ In meeting
- ☐ Asleep
- ☐ Cubicle hopping
- ☐ Who knows
- ☐ ....

CUBICLE ART

☐ Inside the box   ☐ Outside the box

ITEMS TAKEN DURING THIS VISIT:

- ☐ Stapler   ☐ Candy
- ☐ Scissors   ☐ Food
- ☐ Pens   ☐ Medication
- ☐ Toiletries   ☐ Valuables
- ☐ Gum   ☐ ....

ITEMS WERE:

- ☐ Given   ☐ "Borrowed"

TAKEAWAY FROM VISIT:

....

....

REPORT CARD	A	B	C	D	F
Ambience					
Cleanliness					
Décor					
Amenities					
Snacks					
Privacy					
Scuttlebutt					
OVERALL					

Memorable Moments: _____

_____

_____

_____

_____

_____

Additional Sentiments: _____

_____

_____

_____

_____

_____

Welcome to My Cubicle

DATE OF VISIT: ....

TIME OF VISIT: .... AM/PM

TV SHOW THAT BEST DESCRIBES THIS OFFICE:

☐ *Lost*
☐ *Survivor*
☐ *Mad Men*
☐ *Freaks and Geeks*
☐ *The A-Team*
☐ *Modern Family*
☐ ....

CUBICLE ACTIVITY BAR GRAPH

Shade in the amount of time spent doing the following:

	NO TIME	LONG TIME
Liaising		
Strategizing		
Brainstorming		
Procrastinating		
Gossiping		

SIGN IN, PLEASE

REASON FOR VISIT: ☐ Business   ☐ Pleasure   ☐ Boredom

HIDDEN AGENDA: ....

CUBICLE DWELLER WAS:	☐ At desk	☐ On coffee break	☐ Cubicle hopping
	☐ Out to lunch	☐ In meeting	☐ Who knows
	☐ In bathroom	☐ Asleep	☐ ....

CUBICLE ART

☐ Inside the box   ☐ Outside the box

ITEMS TAKEN DURING THIS VISIT:

☐ Stapler   ☐ Candy
☐ Scissors   ☐ Food
☐ Pens   ☐ Medication
☐ Toiletries   ☐ Valuables
☐ Gum   ☐ ....

ITEMS WERE:

☐ Given   ☐ "Borrowed"

TAKEAWAY FROM VISIT:

....
....

REPORT CARD	A	B	C	D	F
Ambience					
Cleanliness					
Décor					
Amenities					
Snacks					
Privacy					
Scuttlebutt					
OVERALL					

Memorable Moments: _____

_____

_____

_____

_____

Additional Sentiments: _____

_____

_____

_____

_____

Welcome to My Cubicle

DATE OF VISIT: ....

TIME OF VISIT: .... AM/PM

TV SHOW THAT BEST DESCRIBES THIS OFFICE:

- ☐ *Lost*
- ☐ *Survivor*
- ☐ *Mad Men*
- ☐ *Freaks and Geeks*
- ☐ *The A-Team*
- ☐ *Modern Family*
- ☐ ....

CUBICLE ACTIVITY BAR GRAPH

Shade in the amount of time spent doing the following:

NO TIME   LONG TIME

Liaising

Strategizing

Brainstorming

Procrastinating

Gossiping

SIGN IN, PLEASE

REASON FOR VISIT: ☐ Business   ☐ Pleasure   ☐ Boredom

HIDDEN AGENDA: ....

CUBICLE DWELLER WAS:
- ☐ At desk
- ☐ Out to lunch
- ☐ In bathroom
- ☐ On coffee break
- ☐ In meeting
- ☐ Asleep
- ☐ Cubicle hopping
- ☐ Who knows
- ☐ ....

CUBICLE ART

☐ Inside the box   ☐ Outside the box

ITEMS TAKEN DURING THIS VISIT:

- ☐ Stapler
- ☐ Scissors
- ☐ Pens
- ☐ Toiletries
- ☐ Gum
- ☐ Candy
- ☐ Food
- ☐ Medication
- ☐ Valuables
- ☐ ....

ITEMS WERE:

- ☐ Given
- ☐ "Borrowed"

TAKEAWAY FROM VISIT:

....
....

REPORT CARD	A	B	C	D	F
Ambience					
Cleanliness					
Décor					
Amenities					
Snacks					
Privacy					
Scuttlebutt					
OVERALL					

Memorable Moments: _____

_____

_____

_____

_____

_____

Additional Sentiments: _____

_____

_____

_____

_____

_____

Welcome to My Cubicle

DATE OF VISIT: ....

TIME OF VISIT: .... AM/PM

TV SHOW THAT BEST DESCRIBES THIS OFFICE:

- ☐ *Lost*
- ☐ *Survivor*
- ☐ *Mad Men*
- ☐ *Freaks and Geeks*
- ☐ *The A-Team*
- ☐ *Modern Family*
- ☐ ....

CUBICLE ACTIVITY BAR GRAPH

Shade in the amount of time spent doing the following:

	NO TIME	LONG TIME
Liaising		
Strategizing		
Brainstorming		
Procrastinating		
Gossiping		

SIGN IN, PLEASE

REASON FOR VISIT: ☐ Business   ☐ Pleasure   ☐ Boredom

HIDDEN AGENDA: ....

CUBICLE DWELLER WAS:	☐ At desk	☐ On coffee break	☐ Cubicle hopping
	☐ Out to lunch	☐ In meeting	☐ Who knows
	☐ In bathroom	☐ Asleep	☐ ....

CUBICLE ART

☐ Inside the box   ☐ Outside the box

ITEMS TAKEN DURING THIS VISIT:

- ☐ Stapler   ☐ Candy
- ☐ Scissors   ☐ Food
- ☐ Pens   ☐ Medication
- ☐ Toiletries   ☐ Valuables
- ☐ Gum   ☐ ....

ITEMS WERE:

☐ Given   ☐ "Borrowed"

TAKEAWAY FROM VISIT:

....
....

REPORT CARD	A	B	C	D	F
Ambience					
Cleanliness					
Décor					
Amenities					
Snacks					
Privacy					
Scuttlebutt					
OVERALL					

Memorable Moments: _____
_____
_____
_____
_____
_____

Additional Sentiments: _____
_____
_____
_____
_____
_____

Welcome to My Cubicle

DATE OF VISIT: ....

TIME OF VISIT: .... AM/PM

TV SHOW THAT BEST DESCRIBES THIS OFFICE:
- ☐ Lost
- ☐ Survivor
- ☐ Mad Men
- ☐ Freaks and Geeks
- ☐ The A-Team
- ☐ Modern Family
- ☐ ....

CUBICLE ACTIVITY BAR GRAPH
Shade in the amount of time spent doing the following:

	NO TIME	LONG TIME
Liaising		
Strategizing		
Brainstorming		
Procrastinating		
Gossiping		

SIGN IN, PLEASE

REASON FOR VISIT: ☐ Business ☐ Pleasure ☐ Boredom

HIDDEN AGENDA: ....

CUBICLE DWELLER WAS:	☐ At desk	☐ On coffee break	☐ Cubicle hopping
	☐ Out to lunch	☐ In meeting	☐ Who knows
	☐ In bathroom	☐ Asleep	☐ ....

CUBICLE ART

☐ Inside the box   ☐ Outside the box

ITEMS TAKEN DURING THIS VISIT:
- ☐ Stapler   ☐ Candy
- ☐ Scissors   ☐ Food
- ☐ Pens   ☐ Medication
- ☐ Toiletries ☐ Valuables
- ☐ Gum   ☐ ....

ITEMS WERE:
☐ Given   ☐ "Borrowed"

TAKEAWAY FROM VISIT:
....
....

REPORT CARD	A	B	C	D	F
Ambience					
Cleanliness					
Décor					
Amenities					
Snacks					
Privacy					
Scuttlebutt					
OVERALL					

Memorable Moments: _____

_____

_____

_____

_____

_____

Additional Sentiments: _____

_____

_____

_____

_____

_____

Welcome to My Cubicle

DATE OF VISIT: ....

TIME OF VISIT: .... AM/PM

TV SHOW THAT BEST DESCRIBES THIS OFFICE:
- ☐ *Lost*
- ☐ *Survivor*
- ☐ *Mad Men*
- ☐ *Freaks and Geeks*
- ☐ *The A-Team*
- ☐ *Modern Family*
- ☐ ....

CUBICLE ACTIVITY BAR GRAPH
Shade in the amount of time spent doing the following:

NO TIME   LONG TIME

Liaising

Strategizing

Brainstorming

Procrastinating

Gossiping

SIGN IN, PLEASE

REASON FOR VISIT: ☐ Business   ☐ Pleasure   ☐ Boredom

HIDDEN AGENDA: ....

CUBICLE DWELLER WAS:
- ☐ At desk
- ☐ Out to lunch
- ☐ In bathroom
- ☐ On coffee break
- ☐ In meeting
- ☐ Asleep
- ☐ Cubicle hopping
- ☐ Who knows
- ☐ ....

CUBICLE ART

☐ Inside the box   ☐ Outside the box

ITEMS TAKEN DURING THIS VISIT:
- ☐ Stapler
- ☐ Scissors
- ☐ Pens
- ☐ Toiletries
- ☐ Gum
- ☐ Candy
- ☐ Food
- ☐ Medication
- ☐ Valuables
- ☐ ....

ITEMS WERE:
- ☐ Given
- ☐ "Borrowed"

TAKEAWAY FROM VISIT:
....
....

REPORT CARD	A	B	C	D	F
Ambience					
Cleanliness					
Décor					
Amenities					
Snacks					
Privacy					
Scuttlebutt					
OVERALL					

Memorable Moments: _____

_____

_____

_____

_____

Additional Sentiments: _____

_____

_____

_____

_____

Welcome to My Cubicle

DATE OF VISIT: ....

TIME OF VISIT: .... AM/PM

TV SHOW THAT BEST DESCRIBES THIS OFFICE:
- ☐ *Lost*
- ☐ *Survivor*
- ☐ *Mad Men*
- ☐ *Freaks and Geeks*
- ☐ *The A-Team*
- ☐ *Modern Family*
- ☐ ....

CUBICLE ACTIVITY BAR GRAPH
Shade in the amount of time spent doing the following:

	NO TIME	LONG TIME
Liaising		
Strategizing		
Brainstorming		
Procrastinating		
Gossiping		

SIGN IN, PLEASE

REASON FOR VISIT: ☐ Business   ☐ Pleasure   ☐ Boredom

HIDDEN AGENDA: ....

CUBICLE DWELLER WAS:	☐ At desk	☐ On coffee break	☐ Cubicle hopping
	☐ Out to lunch	☐ In meeting	☐ Who knows
	☐ In bathroom	☐ Asleep	☐ ....

CUBICLE ART

☐ Inside the box   ☐ Outside the box

ITEMS TAKEN DURING THIS VISIT:
- ☐ Stapler
- ☐ Scissors
- ☐ Pens
- ☐ Toiletries
- ☐ Gum
- ☐ Candy
- ☐ Food
- ☐ Medication
- ☐ Valuables
- ☐ ....

ITEMS WERE:
☐ Given   ☐ "Borrowed"

TAKEAWAY FROM VISIT:
....
....

REPORT CARD	A	B	C	D	F
Ambience					
Cleanliness					
Décor					
Amenities					
Snacks					
Privacy					
Scuttlebutt					
OVERALL					

Memorable Moments: _____

_____

_____

_____

_____

_____

Additional Sentiments: _____

_____

_____

_____

_____

_____

Welcome to My Cubicle

DATE OF VISIT: ....

TIME OF VISIT: .... AM/PM

TV SHOW THAT BEST DESCRIBES THIS OFFICE:
- ☐ *Lost*
- ☐ *Survivor*
- ☐ *Mad Men*
- ☐ *Freaks and Geeks*
- ☐ *The A-Team*
- ☐ *Modern Family*
- ☐ ....

CUBICLE ACTIVITY BAR GRAPH
Shade in the amount of time spent doing the following:

	NO TIME	LONG TIME

Liaising

Strategizing

Brainstorming

Procrastinating

Gossiping

SIGN IN, PLEASE

REASON FOR VISIT: ☐ Business ☐ Pleasure ☐ Boredom

HIDDEN AGENDA: ....

CUBICLE DWELLER WAS:	☐ At desk	☐ On coffee break	☐ Cubicle hopping
	☐ Out to lunch	☐ In meeting	☐ Who knows
	☐ In bathroom	☐ Asleep	☐ ....

CUBICLE ART

☐ Inside the box   ☐ Outside the box

ITEMS TAKEN DURING THIS VISIT:
- ☐ Stapler   ☐ Candy
- ☐ Scissors   ☐ Food
- ☐ Pens   ☐ Medication
- ☐ Toiletries ☐ Valuables
- ☐ Gum   ☐ ....

ITEMS WERE:
- ☐ Given   ☐ "Borrowed"

TAKEAWAY FROM VISIT:
....
....

REPORT CARD	A	B	C	D	F
Ambience					
Cleanliness					
Décor					
Amenities					
Snacks					
Privacy					
Scuttlebutt					
OVERALL					

Memorable Moments: _____
_____
_____
_____
_____
_____

Additional Sentiments: _____
_____
_____
_____
_____
_____

Welcome to My Cubicle

DATE OF VISIT: ....

TIME OF VISIT: .... AM/PM

TV SHOW THAT BEST DESCRIBES THIS OFFICE:

☐ *Lost*
☐ *Survivor*
☐ *Mad Men*
☐ *Freaks and Geeks*
☐ *The A-Team*
☐ *Modern Family*
☐ ....

CUBICLE ACTIVITY BAR GRAPH

Shade in the amount of time spent doing the following:

	NO TIME	LONG TIME
Liaising		
Strategizing		
Brainstorming		
Procrastinating		
Gossiping		

SIGN IN, PLEASE

REASON FOR VISIT: ☐ Business ☐ Pleasure ☐ Boredom

HIDDEN AGENDA: ....

CUBICLE DWELLER WAS:
☐ At desk ☐ On coffee break ☐ Cubicle hopping
☐ Out to lunch ☐ In meeting ☐ Who knows
☐ In bathroom ☐ Asleep ☐ ....

CUBICLE ART

[ ]

☐ Inside the box ☐ Outside the box

ITEMS TAKEN DURING THIS VISIT:

☐ Stapler ☐ Candy
☐ Scissors ☐ Food
☐ Pens ☐ Medication
☐ Toiletries ☐ Valuables
☐ Gum ☐ ....

ITEMS WERE:

☐ Given ☐ "Borrowed"

TAKEAWAY FROM VISIT:

....
....

REPORT CARD	A	B	C	D	F
Ambience					
Cleanliness					
Décor					
Amenities					
Snacks					
Privacy					
Scuttlebutt					
OVERALL					

Memorable Moments: _____

_____

_____

_____

_____

_____

Additional Sentiments: _____

_____

_____

_____

_____

_____

Welcome to My Cubicle

DATE OF VISIT: ....

TIME OF VISIT: .... AM/PM

TV SHOW THAT BEST DESCRIBES THIS OFFICE:
- ☐ *Lost*
- ☐ *Survivor*
- ☐ *Mad Men*
- ☐ *Freaks and Geeks*
- ☐ *The A-Team*
- ☐ *Modern Family*
- ☐ ....

CUBICLE ACTIVITY BAR GRAPH
Shade in the amount of time spent doing the following:

	NO TIME	LONG TIME
Liaising		
Strategizing		
Brainstorming		
Procrastinating		
Gossiping		

SIGN IN, PLEASE

REASON FOR VISIT: ☐ Business ☐ Pleasure ☐ Boredom

HIDDEN AGENDA: ....

CUBICLE DWELLER WAS:
- ☐ At desk
- ☐ Out to lunch
- ☐ In bathroom
- ☐ On coffee break
- ☐ In meeting
- ☐ Asleep
- ☐ Cubicle hopping
- ☐ Who knows
- ☐ ....

CUBICLE ART

☐ Inside the box   ☐ Outside the box

ITEMS TAKEN DURING THIS VISIT:
- ☐ Stapler
- ☐ Scissors
- ☐ Pens
- ☐ Toiletries
- ☐ Gum
- ☐ Candy
- ☐ Food
- ☐ Medication
- ☐ Valuables
- ☐ ....

ITEMS WERE:
- ☐ Given
- ☐ "Borrowed"

TAKEAWAY FROM VISIT:
....
....

REPORT CARD	A	B	C	D	F
Ambience					
Cleanliness					
Décor					
Amenities					
Snacks					
Privacy					
Scuttlebutt					
OVERALL					

Memorable Moments: _____

_____

_____

_____

_____

_____

Additional Sentiments: _____

_____

_____

_____

_____

_____

Welcome to My Cubicle

DATE OF VISIT: ....

TIME OF VISIT: .... AM/PM

TV SHOW THAT BEST DESCRIBES THIS OFFICE:
- ☐ *Lost*
- ☐ *Survivor*
- ☐ *Mad Men*
- ☐ *Freaks and Geeks*
- ☐ *The A-Team*
- ☐ *Modern Family*
- ☐

CUBICLE ACTIVITY BAR GRAPH
Shade in the amount of time spent doing the following:

	NO TIME	LONG TIME

Liaising

Strategizing

Brainstorming

Procrastinating

Gossiping

SIGN IN, PLEASE

REASON FOR VISIT: ☐ Business   ☐ Pleasure   ☐ Boredom

HIDDEN AGENDA: ....

CUBICLE DWELLER WAS:	☐ At desk	☐ On coffee break	☐ Cubicle hopping
	☐ Out to lunch	☐ In meeting	☐ Who knows
	☐ In bathroom	☐ Asleep	☐ ....

CUBICLE ART

☐ Inside the box   ☐ Outside the box

ITEMS TAKEN DURING THIS VISIT:
- ☐ Stapler
- ☐ Scissors
- ☐ Pens
- ☐ Toiletries
- ☐ Gum
- ☐ Candy
- ☐ Food
- ☐ Medication
- ☐ Valuables
- ☐ ....

ITEMS WERE:
☐ Given   ☐ "Borrowed"

TAKEAWAY FROM VISIT:
....
....

REPORT CARD	A	B	C	D	F
Ambience					
Cleanliness					
Décor					
Amenities					
Snacks					
Privacy					
Scuttlebutt					
OVERALL